100 Quick Quizzes

100 Quick Quizzes

Camilla de la Bedoyere

Miles
KeLLY

First published in 2010 as *Flip Quiz: General Knowledge Ages 6–7* by Miles Kelly Publishing Ltd
Harding's Barn, Bardfield End Green, Thaxted, Essex, CM6 3PX, UK

This edition published in 2013

2 4 6 8 10 9 7 5 3 1

Publishing Director Belinda Gallagher
Creative Director Jo Cowan
Assistant Editor Claire Philip
Cover Designer Jo Cowan
Designers Jo Cowan, Joe Jones
Junior Designer Kayleigh Allen
Image Manager Liberty Newton
Production Manager Elizabeth Collins
Reprographics Stephan Davis, Jennifer Hunt, Thom Allaway

ISBN 978-1-78209-122-6

Printed in China

British Library Cataloguing-in-Publication Data
A catalogue record for this book is available from the British Library

ACKNOWLEDGEMENTS
The publishers would like to thank the following sources for the use of their photographs:
COVER **Shutterstock** Ralf Juergen Kraft, Eduardo Rivero
Apple Inc. Quiz 39 **Dreamstime.com** Quiz 10 (2) Jilllang; 12 Razvanjp; 16 Egal; 22 Nruboc; 30 (5) Fragles; 42 Nruboc; 47 Mayangsari; 89 (8) Anna Utekhina, (9) Trix1428; 93 Stefan Hermans **FLPA** Quiz 7 Tui De Roy/Minden Pictures **Fotolia.com** Quiz 2 Jonathan Peat; 9 (8); 10 (10) David Marescaux; 13 V. Yakabchuk; 14 Kristian Peetz; 20 (1), (2) Celso Pupo; 21 alle; 23 Ignatius Wooster; 26 JLV Image Works; 30 (6) James Warren, (8) Luis Carlos Jiménez; 32 Petar Ishmeriev; 35 (l) Dario Sabljak, (r) Michael Flippo; 36 Dariusz Kopestynski; 38 Andreas Meyer; 39 (5) Stephen Coburn, (6) Ivcandy, (9) 2happy, (10) Stefan Balk; 40 (4) Monkey Business, (6), (8) Kiam Soon Jong, (9) Renee Jansoa; 43 Elena Schweitzerl; 44 michanolimit; 50 (1–5) Luisa Venturoli; 54 Urbanhearts; 73 (l) Leonid Smirnov, (r) Uwe Bumann; 80 (4) Joe Gough; 87 Barbara Helgason; 88 Natalia Sinjushina; 89 (1) Ruta Saulyte, (2) Eric Isselée, (4) quayside, (5) Johnny Lye, (10) Kwest; 90 (1) Monika 3 Steps Ahead, (5) Eric Isselée, (10) klikk; 96 Ludovic LAN; 99 (3) treenabeena; 100 (1) Evgeniya Ponomareva, (2) TreePhoto, (3) DE Photography, (4); 71–80 section bars Kiam Soon Jong; 81–90 section bars DE Photography **iStockphoto.com** Quiz 1 Marko Roeper; 8 Andrew Howe; 9 (10) Mark Kostich; 10 (1) coloroftime, (6) Willi Schmitz; 30 (9) Seb Chandler; 40 (7) Rosemarie Gearhart; 58 Linda More; 80 (9) Caziopeia, (10) Owen Price; 90 (7) bojan fatur; 91 Carmen Martínez Banús; 100 (5) Marko Roeper, (8) Chris Crafter, (9) Mark Evans, (10) DNY59 **Moviestorecollection.com** Quiz 97 DreamWorks SKG **Rexfeatures.com** Quiz 24; 72 **Topfoto.co.uk** Quiz 11 Â©ullsteinbild; 78 **The Wildlife Trust** Quiz 10 (3) Philip Precey **The Woodland Trust/Ancient Tree Hunt** Quiz 4 Richard Littlewood (www.ancient-tree-hunt.org.uk)

All other photographs are from: digitalSTOCK, digitalvision, John Foxx, PhotoAlto, PhotoDisc, PhotoEssentials, PhotoPro, Stockbyte
All artwork from the Miles Kelly Artwork Bank

Every effort has been made to acknowledge the source and copyright holder of each picture.
Miles Kelly Publishing apologises for any unintentional errors or omissions.

Made with paper from a sustainable forest

www.mileskelly.net info@mileskelly.net

www.factsforprojects.com

CONTENTS

How to play
Read these pages before you start

Scorecards
Ten scorecards to record your results

HOW TO PLAY

To start

Choose which section you want to play. There are 10 sections, 10 quizzes per section and 10 questions per quiz.

Player/team 1 will always play odd-numbered quizzes – 1, 3, 5, 7 and 9.
Player/team 2 will always play even-numbered quizzes – 2, 4, 6, 8 and 10.

Question & Answer quizzes

Quiz number
There are ten quizzes in each section.

Questions
There are ten questions per quiz.

Illustrated fact
Learn a new fact to amaze your friends.

Flash symbol
This symbol means that the opposite quiz has a Picture clue to help you to answer.

Section heading
There are ten subject sections.

Answers
Cover up the answers before you start.

Picture clue
This image will help you answer a question on the opposite quiz.

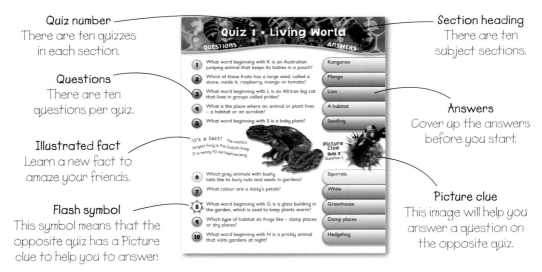

Playing on your own

Cover up the answers before you start. You will play all eight Question & Answer quizzes and fill in your scorecard.

Playing with a friend or in teams

See how Claire and Simon play to help you with your game.

1. Simon covers up Quiz 2 so Claire can't see it while she asks him questions on Quiz 1.
2. Claire asks Simon Questions 1–10 of Quiz 1.
3. For each correct answer, Claire adds a tick to his scorecard. For each incorrect answer, Claire leaves the space blank.
4. Simon asks Claire Questions 1–10 of Quiz 2.
5. Simon fills in Claire's scorecard.
6. Once they have answered all ten questions each, they add up the final score to see who wins that game.

Picture Challenge quizzes

Playing on your own

Cover up the answers before you start. You will play both Picture Challenge quizzes and fill in your scorecard.

Playing with a friend

Claire and Simon reach the last two quizzes in the section, 9 and 10.

1. They cover up the answers before they start.
2. Claire shows Simon the pictures for Quiz 9.
2. Simon writes down his answers on a piece of paper.
3. Claire checks Simon's answers to see how many he has got right and gives him a tick for each correct answer.
4. Then it's Simon's turn to challenge Claire. She will complete Quiz 10.

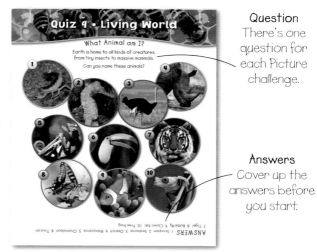

Question
There's one question for each Picture challenge.

Answers
Cover up the answers before you start.

Scorecards

Photocopy the scorecards instead of writing in the book, so you can play again and again. Don't forget – for each section, you'll need one scorecard for each player.

Fill in the quiz numbers.

Add a tick for each correct answer.

Write the player or team name.

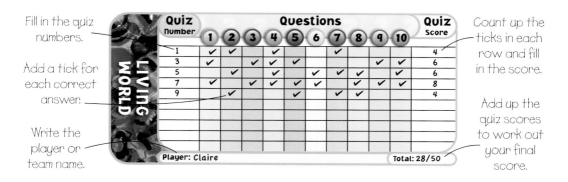

Count up the ticks in each row and fill in the score.

Add up the quiz scores to work out your final score.

Quiz 1 · Living World

1 What word beginning with K is an Australian jumping animal that keeps its babies in a pouch?

Kangaroo

2 Which of these fruits has a large seed, called a stone, inside it: raspberry, mango or tomato?

Mango

3 What word beginning with L is an African big cat that lives in groups called prides?

Lion

4 What is the place where an animal or plant lives – a habitat or an acrobat?

A habitat

5 What word beginning with S is a baby plant?

Seedling

It's a fact! The world's largest frog is the Goliath frog. It is nearly 40 centimetres long.

Picture Clue
Quiz 2
Question 5

6 Which grey animals with bushy tails like to bury nuts and seeds in gardens?

Squirrels

7 What colour are a daisy's petals?

White

8 What word beginning with G is a glass building in the garden, which is used to keep plants warm?

Greenhouse

9 Which type of habitat do frogs like – damp places or dry places?

Damp places

10 What word beginning with H is a prickly animal that visits gardens at night?

Hedgehog

Quiz 2 • Living World

1 I grow in hot places and my little green fruits are used to make a type of oil. What tree am I?

An olive tree

2 What is a seed doing when it is germinating – starting to grow or starting to die?

Starting to grow

3 What does the word 'extinct' mean – very rare or died out forever?

Died out forever

4 Where would you find chimps living – in a forest or in a desert?

In a forest

5 What is the fruit of a horse chestnut tree called – a pea pod or a conker?

A conker

It's a fact! Flowers are brightly coloured to attract insects to them. The insects pollinate the flowers, so the plants can grow seeds.

Picture Clue
Quiz 1
Question 8

6 What is a baby frog called?

A tadpole

7 Which of these fruits grow on vines – grapes or plums?

Grapes

8 What word beginning with E is the largest animal on land?

Elephant

9 What colour is a daffodil?

Yellow

10 What word beginning with S is the crumbly brown substance that plants grow in?

Soil

Quiz 3 • Living World

1 Do plants grow towards light, or away from it?

Towards light

2 Where would you be more likely to find white animals — in a snowy habitat or a jungle habitat?

A snowy habitat

3 What word beginning with P is a farm animal that lives in a sty?

Pig

4 I have spiky green leaves and red berries, and I am used as decoration at Christmas — what am I?

Holly

5 What word beginning with P is the fine yellow powder found inside a flower?

Pollen

It's a fact! Slugs and snails belong to the same animal family as squid and octopuses. They are all molluscs, and they do not have backbones.

Picture Clue
Quiz 4
Question 2

6 I am slimy like a slug, but I have a shell to protect my soft body — what am I?

A snail

7 What is the name of the world's tallest bird — ostrich or penguin?

Ostrich

8 What word beginning with C is a farm animal that lays eggs?

Chicken

9 What is a baby butterfly called?

A caterpillar

10 What word beginning with G is the tallest animal in the world?

Giraffe

Quiz 4 • Living World

1 Which of these animals is not a mammal: dolphin, human, eagle or rat?

Eagle

2 What word beginning with S is a slithering, scaly reptile that has no legs?

Snake

3 What does a root do – collect sugar from the soil or take in water?

Take in water

4 What word beginning with O is a night bird with large eyes?

Owl

5 What name is given to young goats – kids or foals?

Kids

It's a fact! You can find out how old trees are by hugging them, because trees get fatter as they age. Many oak and yew trees are hundreds of years old.

Picture Clue
Quiz 3
Question 8

6 What word beginning with M is a living thing that grows on old or rotten food?

Mould

7 I live for hundreds of years and my fruits are called acorns. What tree am I?

An oak tree

8 What word beginning with T is a stripy big cat that is in danger of becoming extinct?

Tiger

9 What word beginning with L is a red beetle with black spots?

Ladybird

10 I have eight legs, I build webs and I eat flies. What am I?

A spider

Quiz 5 • Living World

1 What name is given to young dogs?

Puppies

2 I am a large bear and my thick white fur keeps me warm in my Arctic home. What kind of bear am I?

A polar bear

3 What word beginning with B are tiny living things that grow on dirty surfaces and can cause illness?

Bacteria

4 I have feathers and I lay eggs. What type of animal am I?

A bird

5 Can penguins fly?

No

It's a fact! Bacteria and viruses are tiny living things that are everywhere, but invisible to us. Some can cause diseases, which is why washing your hands is important.

Picture Clue
Quiz 6
Question 10

6 How many legs does an octopus have?

Eight

7 What name is given to young fish — fry or boil?

Fry

8 What word beginning with S is a horse's shelter?

Stable

9 Which is bigger — a rabbit or a hare?

A hare

10 What colourless liquid do plants need to grow?

Water

Quiz 6 • Living World

1 When did dinosaurs die out – 65 million years ago or 65 thousand years ago?

65 million years ago

2 What word beginning with R is the first part of a plant to grow from a seed?

Root

3 Which word beginning with S is a juicy red fruit that has seeds growing on the outside?

Strawberry

4 Which of these animals is not a mini-beast: beetle, fly, wallaby or spider?

Wallaby

5 I am green and I am the part of a plant where food is made. What am I?

A leaf

It's a fact! One of the largest dinosaurs was Brachiosaurus. This huge plant-eater measured up to 25 metres from nose to tail.

Picture Clue
Quiz 5
Question 1

6 Which animal does not live in or near a pond: frog, water beetle, seahorse, newt?

Seahorse – it lives in the sea

7 What word is the plural for a group of horses – a herd or a flock?

A herd

8 What word beginning with S is the first part of a plant that grows upwards towards the light?

Shoot

9 Which animals have scales and fins, and use gills to breathe?

Fish

10 Some animals sleep through winter. Is this called hibernation or migration?

Hibernation

Quiz 7 • Living World

QUESTIONS

ANSWERS

1 Which of these birds cannot swim: sparrow, penguin or goose?

Sparrow

2 What word beginning with W is a liquid that we drink to stop us getting thirsty?

Water

3 Which juicy black fruits grow on bramble bushes?

Blackberries

4 Which animal has a backbone: toad, octopus or starfish?

Toad

5 I grow from flowers, and when I fall to the soil I may grow into a new plant. What am I?

A seed

It's a fact! Lonesome George was a giant tortoise, and the last member of his species. When he died in June 2012, his species (called the Abingdon Island tortoise) became extinct.

Picture Clue
Quiz 8
Question 7

6 Where do lizards lay their eggs – on land or in water?

On land

7 Is a shark a whale or a fish?

A fish

8 What word beginning with P is the name for the coloured outside parts of a flower?

Petals

9 Which of these things is not alive: badger, beetroot, book, baby?

Book

10 Can dolphins breathe underwater, or do they hold their breath?

They hold their breath

Quiz 8 • Living World

1 What is the largest animal alive today?

The blue whale

2 What is a flower called before it opens up fully – a pod or a bud?

A bud

3 Is a moth a type of insect or a type of reptile?

An insect

4 What is a female horse called – a mare or a nanny?

A mare

5 Do whiskers help a cat with its sense of smell or its sense of touch?

Its sense of touch

It's a fact! Soil may look like mud, but it is packed with tiny creatures, water, air and lots of other good things that all help plants to grow.

Picture Clue
Quiz 7
Question 1

6 Did dinosaurs lay eggs?

Yes

7 Which of these animals is not a type of bear: panda, anteater, polar, black?

Anteater

8 What word beginning with S is a garden tool you would use for digging soil?

Spade, or shovel

9 Where do frogs lay their eggs – in water or on land?

In water

10 What word beginning with E is a wriggly garden animal that burrows through soil?

Earthworm

Quiz 9 • Living World

What Animal am I?

Earth is home to all kinds of creatures,
from tiny insects to massive mammals.

Can you name these animals?

Quiz 10 • Living World

What Flower am I?

Many flowers are easy to spot because they have bright colours to attract bees and other animals.

Can you name these flowers?

Quiz 11 • Healthy Living

QUESTIONS

ANSWERS

1 What word beginning with S is another word for a backbone?

Spine

2 I am packed with protein and vitamins, have a shell and come from a hen. What am I?

An egg

3 Which part of your face do you use for smelling things?

Your nose

4 What word beginning with Y is a spinning toy that is attached to a string, and goes up and down?

Yo-yo

5 Is your elbow a joint or a muscle?

A joint

It's a fact! Michael Phelps is the world's greatest swimmer. He won eight gold medals at the Beijing Olympics in 2008. Michael took up swimming when he was seven years old.

Picture Clue
Quiz 12
Question 1

6 If women and girls are females, what are men and boys?

Males

7 Which type of exercise will make your heart beat faster – skipping or walking?

Skipping

8 Which bread has more fibre in it – wholemeal or white?

Wholemeal

9 Which word beginning with E is the shiny hard part of your teeth?

Enamel

10 Which of these sports does not need a racket or bat: tennis, basketball or badminton?

Basketball

Quiz 12 • Healthy Living

QUESTIONS

ANSWERS

1 What word beginning with P is used to describe a woman who has a baby growing inside her?

Pregnant

2 What word beginning with L is the name of the body parts that humans use to breathe?

Lungs

3 Is mackerel a type of fish, a fruit or a sponge cake?

A fish

4 Which ball game is played by teams that want to score 'tries'?

Rugby

5 What word beginning with S helps to clean your hands?

Soap

It's a fact! In the UK, we can expect to live for 75 years or more, if we lead healthy lives. In poorer countries, where it can be harder to live a healthy life, people often have shorter lifespans.

Picture Clue
Quiz 11
Question 7

6 Which of these foods are not carbohydrates – bread, rice, pasta or cheese?

Cheese

7 Which of these vegetables is not green: pea, sweet potato or courgette?

Sweet potato

8 If your heart beats 100 times in one minute, how many times will it beat in five minutes?

500

9 Which teeth are best for chewing tough food – incisors or molars?

Molars

10 Which long yellow fruit has an easy-to-peel skin?

Banana

Quiz 13 • Healthy Living

QUESTIONS

ANSWERS

1 Which body part breaks down food into smaller bits – the stomach or the kidneys?

The stomach

2 Which diet is healthy – one with lots of different types of food, or one with lots of chips?

One with lots of different food

3 I am a small, green and hairy fruit that is packed with Vitamin C. What am I?

A kiwi fruit

4 In what sport would you do forward rolls and cartwheels?

Gymnastics

5 Which body part in your chest pumps blood around your body?

Your heart

It's a fact! Just one drop of blood contains about 5 million – that's 5,000,000 – red blood cells. These cells carry oxygen to all the parts of your body.

Picture Clue
Quiz 14
Question 1

6 What word beginning with B describes the taking in of air through your mouth or nose?

Breathe or breathing

7 If you jump off a high board, would you be diving or trampolining?

Diving

8 What do newborn babies mostly drink?

Milk

9 What is the name of the red liquid that travels through your body in tubes called vessels?

Blood

10 What word beginning with P would you put over a cut to protect it from germs?

Plaster

Quiz 14 • Healthy Living

1 What word beginning with D is a person who helps sick people to get well and stay healthy?

Doctor

2 Which drink gives you more calcium – fruit juice or milk?

Milk

3 Ben says he can do the crawl, the backstroke and the butterfly. What is Ben's sport?

Swimming

4 What is a vegetarian?

Someone who does not eat meat or fish

5 Finish this rhyming phrase: coughs and sneezes spread...

Diseases

It's a fact! Everyone needs Vitamin D to turn calcium into strong bones and teeth. You can get it from sunshine and some foods. Without Vitamin D you can develop rickets, or soft bones.

Picture Clue
QUIZ 13
Question 3

6 What word beginning with B is a yellow spread made from cows' milk?

Butter

7 Which of these things is low in sugar: fizzy drinks, carrots or sweets?

Carrots

8 Sam swims 50 metres when he swims one length of the pool. How far will he swim in two lengths?

100 metres

9 What word beginning with R describes food that has not been cooked?

Raw

10 I am a type of pasta. I am long and thin and I taste delicious with Bolognese sauce – what am I?

Spaghetti

Quiz 15 • Healthy Living

QUESTIONS

ANSWERS

1 How many senses do humans have?

Five

2 What medical gadget would a doctor use to find out if you have a temperature?

A thermometer

3 I am a white vegetable, and often served in cheese sauce. My name ends in 'flower'. What am I?

Cauliflower

4 Which sport is played with small bats and is sometimes called ping-pong?

Table tennis

5 What word beginning with S is the joint that connects your arm to your body?

Shoulder

It's a fact! Humans have a good sense of smell, but it doesn't compare to a dog's. Some dogs can match a person to their clothes, just by smell!

Picture Clue
Quiz 16
Question 5

6 I'm an orange root vegetable packed with a vitamin that is good for your eyesight. What am I?

A carrot

7 Which part of the body do you use for thinking?

Your brain

8 What word beginning with D is the person who helps us to look after our teeth?

Dentist

9 What piece of safety equipment do cyclists wear to protect their heads?

Helmet

10 What word beginning with P is the rhythmic beat caused by blood being pumped around your body?

Pulse

Quiz 16 • Healthy Living

QUESTIONS

ANSWERS

1 Which of these body parts is not an organ: brain, kidney, rib cage or stomach?

Rib cage

2 How often should you visit a dentist — every six months or every two years?

Every six months

3 Which of these sports does not use a ball: netball, hockey, judo or golf?

Judo

4 What is the odd one out: seeing, hearing, talking, touching, tasting or smelling?

Talking

5 What word beginning with B is an American game similar to rounders?

Baseball

It's a fact! Henry the Eighth loved playing tennis so much that he built new courts at Hampton Court Palace in 1625. At the time, tennis was played in a room and players hit the ball against the walls.

Picture Clue
QUIZ 15
Question 3

6 What word beginning with E is an activity to keep your heart healthy?

Exercise

7 How many hours of exercise should you do every day: ten minutes, one hour or three hours?

One hour

8 What controls your whole body — your brain or your heart?

Your brain

9 How many portions of fruit and vegetables should everyone aim to eat every day?

At least five

10 What word beginning with C is a disease that can be caused by smoking cigarettes?

Cancer

Quiz 17 • Healthy Living

QUESTIONS

ANSWERS

1 There are 32 of us in a grown-up's mouth and we help people to bite and chew. What are we?

Teeth

2 What word beginning with T is a very young child that has just learnt to walk?

Toddler

3 What word beginning with P is a large spiky fruit with sweet yellow flesh inside?

Pineapple

4 Why do people sweat in hot weather – to get thirsty or to cool down?

To cool down

5 I have big, green leaves and am often used in salads. What am I?

Lettuce

It's a fact! Many Roman emperors loved eating too much. They had a special room, called a vomitorium, where people made themselves sick, so they could eat even more!

Picture Clue
Quiz 18
Question 3

6 Which of these foods has lots of fat: butter, broccoli, beans or bananas?

Butter

7 Which part of your body do you use for seeing?

Your eyes

8 We are inside your body. We move your bones and exercise makes us stronger. What are we?

Muscles

9 How many players are there in a football team?

Eleven

10 How often should you brush your teeth?

At least twice a day

Quiz 18 • Healthy Living

1 I grow on people's heads and can be long, short, curly or straight – what am I?

Hair

2 Which of these is not a citrus fruit: orange, apple, grapefruit or satsuma?

Apple

3 What is the name for the short hairs on your eyelids?

Eyelashes

4 What would you eat to get more iron in your diet – meat or potatoes?

Meat

5 What word beginning with H is made by bees and spread on bread?

Honey

It's a fact! Ostrich eggs are huge, but they can still be used in cooking. An ostrich egg omelette is the same size as one made from about 24 hens' eggs!

Picture Clue
Quiz 17
Question 8

6 What word beginning with B is a type of dance in which people stand on the tips of their toes?

Ballet

7 Are your ribs made of bone or muscle?

Bone

8 You can boil me, roast me, fry me, bake me and mash me. What am I?

A potato

9 What are the small openings in your nose called?

Nostrils

10 What word beginning with R is a list of instructions that tells you how to cook something?

Recipe

Quiz 19 • Healthy Living

Body Parts

Your body is like a very complicated machine, with lots of parts all doing different jobs.

Can you name the labelled parts?

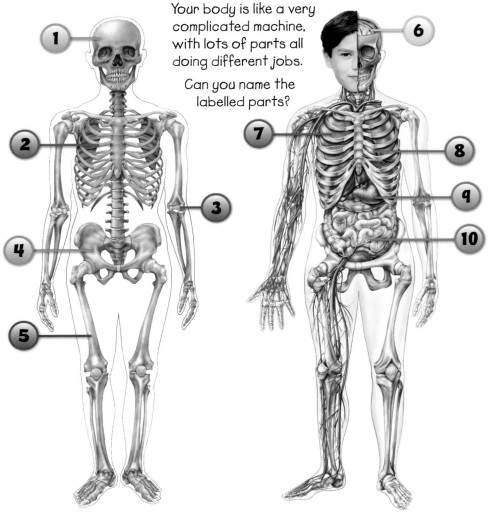

Quiz 20 • Healthy Living

Sorting Food

What type of foods are these – carbohydrates or proteins?

1. Potatoes
2. Beef
3. Chicken
4. Bread
5. Pasta
6. Cheese
7. Fish
8. Eggs
9. Rice
10. Cereal

Quiz 21 • Wonderful Words

QUESTIONS

ANSWERS

1 Finish this phrase: "Once upon a ..."

Time

2 What is the opposite of hard?

Soft

3 What word beginning with R describes two or more words that have the same final sounds?

Rhyme or rhyming

4 Spell the word 'July'.

July

5 Which famous egg fell off a wall, and couldn't be mended?

Humpty Dumpty

It's a fact! The Romans wrote lots of information books and storybooks, and they also wrote joke books. One, called Laughter Lover, is 1600 years old.

Picture Clue
QUIZ 22
Question 8

6 Finish this sentence from the famous book of the same name: 'We're going on a ...'

Bear hunt

7 What is the tenth letter of the alphabet?

J

8 How many dwarfs did Snow White meet?

Seven

9 Which two days make up the weekend?

Saturday and Sunday

10 If something is described as 'gruesome' is it horrible or gorgeous?

Horrible

Quiz 22 • Wonderful Words

1 Is 'pretty' a doing word or a describing word?

A describing word

2 Which monster with 'terrible tusks' did a mouse find in a 'deep, dark wood'?

The Gruffalo

3 What is the name of Hansel's sister?

Gretel

4 What word beginning with S is the opposite of big?

Small

5 Which word is the odd one out: bright, night, glitter, fight?

Glitter

It's a fact! You do not have to write, or speak, words. People who are deaf use sign language – they communicate using gestures, facial expressions and body language.

C

Picture Clue
Quiz 21
Question 5

6 What book would you use to find out what a word means?

A dictionary

7 How many letters are in the word 'computer'?

Eight

8 What word beginning with A is the group of animals that frogs and toads belong to?

Amphibian

9 Who climbed a beanstalk and found a giant?

Jack

10 Spell the word 'school'.

School

Quiz 23 • Wonderful Words

QUESTIONS

1 Which word is the odd one out: blue, new, red, glue?

2 What type of 'stop' would you put at the end of a sentence?

3 Which word best describes the wolf that Red Riding Hood met — wicked or wonderful?

4 Who writes books — authors or artists?

5 What is the opposite of clean?

It's a fact! In Greek myths, Atlas was a god who was made to carry the skies on his shoulders. The word 'atlas' is used for books of maps because of this story.

6 Which month comes after September?

7 What is the 15th letter of the alphabet?

8 What did Goldilocks eat in the bears' house?

9 What word beginning with T comes after first and second, and before fourth?

10 Is an atlas an information book, or a storybook?

ANSWERS

Red

A full stop

Wicked

Authors

Dirty

Picture Clue
Quiz 24
Question 2

October

O

Porridge

Third

An information book

Quiz 24 • Wonderful Words

QUESTIONS

ANSWERS

1 Is 'dancing' a doing word or a describing word?

A doing word

2 How many ugly sisters did Cinderella have?

Two

3 Spell the word 'teeth'.

Teeth

4 Did Roald Dahl write *Fantastic Mr Fox*, or *Fabulous Mr Frog*?

Fantastic Mr Fox

5 How many syllables are in the word 'umbrella'?

Three: um-bre-lla

It's a fact! Roald Dahl wrote his books sitting in a shed in his garden. One of his most famous stories is Fantastic Mr Fox, which was made into a film in 2009.

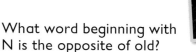

Picture Clue
Quiz 23
Question 8

6 What word beginning with N is the opposite of old?

New

7 What do you call someone who writes poetry?

A poet

8 What is the plural of the word 'wife'?

Wives

9 What happens to fairy tale frogs when they are kissed?

They turn into princes

10 What word beginning with S is a little wooden shelter that is found in the garden?

Shed

Quiz 25 • Wonderful Words

1 What word beginning with V is a person who cares for sick animals?

Vet, or veterinary surgeon

2 What type of letter should you begin every sentence with?

A capital letter

3 Spell the word 'black'.

Black

4 Which word is the odd one out: class, school, glass, grass?

School

5 What is a baby cat called?

A kitten

It's a fact! English words that are used in other countries where English is not the national language, are called 'loanwords'. 'Football', 'hamburger' and 'cinema' are all loanwords.

Picture Clue
Quiz 26
Question 6

6 Does messy mean untidy or ugly?

Untidy

7 What punctuation mark would you use at the end of a question?

A question mark

8 What word beginning with D is the opposite of wet?

Dry

9 What word, which rhymes with cap, describes a short sleep?

Nap

10 Who ate Baby Bear's porridge?

Goldilocks

Quiz 26 • Wonderful Words

QUESTIONS

ANSWERS

1. Which of these words starts with a silent 'k': knuckle, nowhere, nappy?

   Knuckle

2. What time was it when Cinderella's clothes turned to rags?

   Midnight

3. What word beginning with H is the opposite of sad?

   Happy

4. Which type of punctuation mark shows that someone is speaking?

   Speech marks, or quotation marks

5. Which eight-legged animal scared Little Miss Muffet?

   A spider

It's a fact! English is full of words that have come from other countries. The word 'pyjamas' comes from India, 'banana' is an African word, and 'ice cream sundae' comes from the USA.

Picture Clue
Quiz 25
Question 10

6. What type of scary creature lived under the bridge that the goats wanted to cross?

   A troll

7. What word beginning with D means 12 of something, such as eggs?

   Dozen

8. Which word is the odd one out: lovely, kind, hurtful, nice?

   Hurtful

9. Finish this famous question from *Snow White and the Seven Dwarfs*: 'Mirror, mirror, on the wall ...'

   Who's the fairest of them all?

10. What is the plural of the word 'mouse'?

    Mice

1 How many years did Sleeping Beauty spend asleep before the Prince woke her?

100

2 Which is the odd one out: soap, rope, hope, soup?

Soup

3 What word beginning with T is a type of cooked bread that goes well with baked beans?

Toast

4 Which Doctor wrote *The Cat in the Hat* books?

Dr Seuss

5 What is the opposite of night?

Day

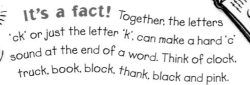

It's a fact! Together, the letters 'ck' or just the letter 'k', can make a hard 'c' sound at the end of a word. Think of clock, truck, book, block, thank, black and pink.

Picture Clue
Quiz 28
Question 9

6 Is 'running' a doing word or a describing word?

A doing word

7 What word beginning with E is made of paper and is used to send letters?

Envelope

8 How did the witch reach Rapunzel in her tall tower?

She climbed up Rapunzel's hair

9 What word beginning with C is a yellow dairy food that is delicious in sandwiches?

Cheese

10 Who took Wendy to Neverland?

Peter Pan

Quiz 28 • Wonderful Words

QUESTIONS

ANSWERS

1 What type of animal was Mog, who featured in Judith Kerr's famous books?

A cat

2 How many letters are in the word 'pavement'?

Eight

3 What building do you visit when you want to borrow books?

A library

4 What special type of writing is Benjamin Zephaniah famous for?

Poetry

5 What word beginning with O is a type of monster?

Ogre

It's a fact! One of the most famous fictional cats is the smiling Cheshire cat, which appears (and disappears!) in Alice's Adventures in Wonderland.

Picture Clue
Quiz 27
Question 10

6 What word, which rhymes with frizzle, means light rain?

Drizzle

7 What name is given to a page at the beginning of a book, which lists all of its chapters?

Contents

8 What day comes after Thursday?

Friday

9 What character in *The Wind in the Willows* buys a horse-drawn caravan and a motor car?

Mr Toad

10 What word beginning with C is the opposite of hot?

Cold

ANSWERS 1. Incy Wincy Spider 2. Mary had a Little Lamb 3. There was an Old Woman Who Lived in a Shoe 4. Jack and Jill 5. Jack Be Nimble 6. Three Men in a Tub 7. Little Bo-Peep 8. Baa Baa Black Sheep 9. Rock-a-Bye Baby 10. Wee Willie Winkie

Rhyme Time

Do you know the names of these nursery rhymes?

Quiz 30 • Wonderful Words

Spot the Rhyme

Rhyming words have endings that
sound similar – such as can and van.

Can you find the matching pairs of
rhyming words?

1

2

3

4

5

6

7

8

q

10

ANSWERS 1 and 9 (Pie and Eye), 2 and 3 (Tree and Bee), 4 and 8 (Fox and Socks), 5 and 7 (Cat and Hat), 6 and 10 (Frog and Dog)

Quiz 31 • Super Science

1 Is glass hard or soft?

Hard

2 Where does daylight come from?

The Sun

3 Will stretching something make it longer or shorter?

Longer

4 Does plastic grow on trees?

No, it's made in a factory

5 Which flies fastest – a kite, a plane or a pigeon?

A plane

It's a fact! The Sun is the closest star to Earth, and the brightest object in the sky. We have to be careful not to look at it directly as it can damage our eyes.

Picture Clue
Quiz 32
Question 8

6 What word beginning with S is what our ears detect?

Sound

7 Which object needs a battery to work: a mobile phone, a magnifying glass or a tumble dryer?

A mobile phone

8 Are rubber gloves waterproof, flexible, or both?

Both

9 What word beginning with T means see-through?

Transparent

10 What has batteries, a bulb and can be used to help us see in the dark?

A torch

Quiz 32 • Super Science

1 What makes the quietest sound: shouting, breathing or snoring?

> Breathing

2 Is lifting your foot from the floor a push or a pull?

> A pull

3 Does water on a slide make you go faster or slower?

> Faster

4 James wears a blindfold to play a party game. What word beginning with L can't he see?

> Light

5 Which would you be able to move by blowing through a straw – a football or a ping-pong ball?

> A ping-pong ball

It's a fact! Dogs can hear dog whistles that are too high-pitched for human ears, so we hear nothing at all. As we get older, our ears aren't so good at hearing high-pitched sounds.

Picture Clue
Quiz 31
Question 10

6 What word beginning with B supplies the electricity for a television remote control?

> Battery

7 What describes how high or low a sound is – the pitch or the patch?

> The pitch

8 Which of these musical instruments have strings: a cello, an oboe or a cymbal?

> A cello

9 Which is shinier – a towel or a diamond?

> A diamond

10 What will happen to a bar of chocolate if you leave it in the hot sunshine?

> It will melt

Quiz 33 • Super Science

QUESTIONS	ANSWERS

1 Which reflects light better – a mirror or a piece of wood?

A mirror

2 What word beginning with I is frozen water that can make roads and pavements slippery?

Ice

3 Which of these does not describe a newspaper: bendy, waterproof or smooth?

Waterproof

4 We give off heat and light and you put us on birthday cakes. What are we?

Candles

5 What word beginning with S means there is no sound?

Silent or silence

It's a fact! Icebergs are huge floating blocks of ice. Most of an iceberg is underwater, so they're much bigger than they look. This is where the expression 'tip of the iceberg' comes from.

Picture Clue
Quiz 34
Question 10

6 What do we call something that can make things speed up and slow down – a force or a farce?

A force

7 What word beginning with B is the opposite of dim?

Bright

8 If a boat has sails, what do the sails trap to move the boat through the water?

Wind

9 Which instrument do you blow through to make a sound: a flute, a guitar or a bongo drum?

A flute

10 What are car tyres made from – rubber or wood?

Rubber

Quiz 34 • Super Science

1 Will a magnet attract a plastic bag?

No

2 Which is harder – a raw egg or a cooked egg?

A cooked egg

3 What turns an electrical circuit on and off – a battery or a switch?

A switch

4 Which uses a twist – unscrewing a lid or patting a dog?

Unscrewing a lid

5 Ben is pushing an empty shopping trolley and Jess is pushing a full one. Who has to push harder?

Jess

It's a fact! The basic design of the bicycle has hardly changed for more than 100 years. It is made up of simple devices such as wheels, pulleys, gears, axles and springs.

Picture Clue
Quiz 33
Question 4

6 Which material is not found underground: paper, water or oil?

Paper

7 Can we see forces?

No, we can only see what they do

8 Which of these objects would float in water: an apple, a stone or a sponge?

The apple and the sponge would float

9 Where would ice cream melt faster – in a hot oven or a cold fridge?

A hot oven

10 What word beginning with P is the part of a bicycle you push down on with your foot?

Pedal

Quiz 35 • Super Science

1 What word beginning with R is the opposite of smooth?

Rough

2 How do you make louder beats on a drum?

By beating it harder

3 What does gravity do – pull things towards the centre of the Earth, or push them into space?

It pulls them towards Earth's centre

4 Does a bar of soap float or sink in water?

Sink

5 Which sound has a higher pitch – a baby's cry or a cat's purr?

A baby's cry

It's a fact! Wool is a warm, soft material made from the hair of sheep and some other animals. It can be used to make clothes.

Picture Clue
Quiz 36
Question 9

6 Which is softer – metal or wool?

Wool

7 Which is easiest to break: a glass bottle, a metal spoon or a woolly hat?

A glass bottle

8 Is a sparkly necklace a source of light?

No, but it does reflect light

9 How do you turn water into steam?

By boiling it

10 Does water boil at 100 degrees Centigrade or 50 degrees Centigrade?

100 degrees Centigrade

Quiz 36 • Super Science

1 What word beginning with T is a large woody plant that is used to make paper?

Tree

2 Can toast be turned back into bread?

No

3 What will make the least sound from a tambourine: hitting it, blowing on it or shaking it?

Blowing on it

4 Which word does not describe a movement: swerve, hold, hop or spin?

Hold

5 Kyle goes downhill on his roller blades. When the slope gets steeper, does he go faster or slower?

Faster

It's a fact! Most car engines run on petrol. Using petrol makes gases that pollute the air (make it dirty). Some cars now use electricity instead of petrol as a cleaner way of powering their engines.

Picture Clue
Quiz 35
Question 9

6 Which of these things is not made by humans: a plank of wood, a twig or a wooden spoon?

A twig

7 If you play your music at top volume, is it loud or quiet?

Loud

8 Would a magnet attract a piece of paper?

No

9 How many wheels would you find on a tricycle?

Three

10 Do most cars have their engines in the boot or under the bonnet?

Under the bonnet

Quiz 37 · Super Science

1 Is a soft sound quiet or loud?

Quiet

2 In a tug of war, team A and team B are pulling with exactly the same force. Which team is winning?

Neither team is winning – it is a draw.

3 Which of these is not a fossil fuel: petrol, olive oil or coal?

Olive oil

4 Can sound travel through water?

Yes

5 What are frying pans made from – metal or wood?

Metal

It's a fact! Coal is found deep underground. When the first steam engines were invented in the 18th century, they used coal, which was burnt to produce steam.

Picture Clue
Quiz 38
Question 5

6 Which is better for sliding on – a smooth surface or a rough surface?

A smooth surface

7 Is a water bottle waterproof?

Yes

8 What word beginning with A does wood turn into when you burn it?

Ash

9 What word beginning with W would you use to join a battery and a bulb in an electrical circuit?

Wire

10 Which sound has a lower pitch – a dog's bark or a bird's song?

A dog's bark

Quiz 38 • Super Science

1 Why does a smoke alarm sound – to warn of fire or to make grown-ups stop smoking cigarettes?

To warn of fire

2 What word beginning with R is another word for stone?

Rock

3 Finish the sentence: Don't play with electrical sockets because they might give you an electric...

Shock

4 Which bends more easily – glass or rope?

Rope

5 What word beginning with M describes something that is attracted to a magnet?

Magnetic

It's a fact! Fireworks were invented in China nearly 1000 years ago. The materials inside them burn to make noise, light, heat and smoke. Fireworks are used in displays all over the world.

Picture Clue
Quiz 37
Question 9

6 When do firework displays look best – at night or in the day?

At night

7 What word beginning with S is made by caterpillars and is then woven into a soft fabric?

Silk

8 Can electricity travel along a metal wire?

Yes

9 Which will sink first – a piece of wood or a bunch of keys?

A bunch of keys

10 When David Beckham kicks a football, is he using a push force or a pull force?

A push force

Electric or Not?

Electricity powers all sorts of machines,
many of which we use every day.

Which of these things run
on electric power?

1

2

3

4

5

6

7

8

9

10

ANSWERS Yes = 1. Torch 3. Mobile phone 7. Light bulb 9. Microwave 10. Electric guitar
No = 2. Bike 4. Pull-along toy 5. Telescope 6. Kayak 8. Violin

Push or Pull?

Pushes and pulls are forces that can make things move, stop, or change direction.

Do these activities use a push, a pull or both?

1

2

3

4

5

6

7

8

q

10

ANSWERS Pushes = 2. Kicking a ball 4. Typing 6. Playing the piano 10. Golf Both = 1. Climbing 5. Swimming 8. Rowing Pulls = 3. Picking an apple 7. Tug-of-war 9. Pulling a suitcase

Quiz 41 • Number Crunchers

1 Toby has 6 apples, and gives his sister half of them. How many does he keep?

3

2 What number is three more than five?

8

3 What is the missing number: 4 + ? = 20

16

4 If Ben draws around the bottom of his cup, what shape will he have drawn – a circle or a square?

A circle

5 What would you use to measure your height – a ruler or a jug?

A ruler

It's a fact! A circle is a very simple shape. The distance all the way around a circle is called its circumference. A circle has no corners or angles. A 3D circle is called a sphere.

Picture Clue
Quiz 42
Question 8

6 How many sides does a triangle have?

3

7 What is 2 + 2 + 2 + 2 + 2?

10

8 What is 10 less than 32?

22

9 A robin lays 6 eggs and a blackbird lays 5. How many eggs are there altogether?

11

10 Billy measures two caterpillars. The red one is 3 centimetres and the green one is 12 millimetres. Which one is longest?

The red one

Quiz 42 • number Crunchers

1 Rosie's birthday is on Friday. Her brother Tom's birthday is three days later. What day will that be?

Monday

2 What is the missing number: 20 − 11 = ?

9

3 Yasmin pours half a litre of water into a one-litre jug. How much more water will fit in the jug?

Half a litre, or 500 millilitres

4 Which of these shapes has the most sides: triangle, pentagon or square?

A pentagon – it is a five-sided shape

5 What is 10 less than 30?

20

It's a fact! We probably count in tens because we have ten fingers. Long ago, when people first started to count, they used their hands to help them.

Picture Clue
Quiz 41
Question 6

6 What is the next number in this sequence: 10, 9, 8, 7…?

6

7 April has one less day than March, which has 31 days. How many days are in April?

30

8 Katie has bought 10 cakes. She gives half of them to her friend. How many cakes are left?

5

9 What is the missing number: 15 + ? = 20

5

10 Baljit has £2 pocket money and she spends £1.50. How much money does she have left?

50 pence

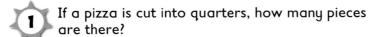

QUESTIONS   **ANSWERS**

1 If a pizza is cut into quarters, how many pieces are there?

4

2 A man walks around a square field. One side is one kilometre. How far does the man walk?

4 kilometres

3 What is 2 less than 19?

17

4 Joe has 4 sweets. He eats one-quarter of them. How many sweets does Joe have now?

3

5 How many right angles are there in a rectangle?

Four

It's a fact! Even numbers can be put into groups of two, with nothing left over. They always end with one of these digits: 0, 2, 4, 6 or 8. If a number isn't even, it is odd!

Picture Clue
Quiz 44
Question 7

6 The children are walking in pairs. If there are 10 pairs, how many children are there altogether?

20

7 One apple costs 50 pence. How much will two apples cost?

£1

8 What unit would you use to measure the depth of a swimming pool – metres or kilograms?

Metres

9 I am round, I have no straight lines and I am a good shape for a wheel. What shape am I?

A circle

10 Which of these numbers is even: 3, 5, 6, 7, 9?

6

Quiz 44 • Number Crunchers

1 What is 2 less than 100?

98

2 Joey scores six goals, but Jess scores twice as many. How many goals does Jess score?

12

3 Annie had 20 pence in her pocket, but she lost 5 pence. How much does she have left?

15 pence

4 Double 10, take away 5. What are you left with?

15

5 Grandad is 75 years old, but Granny is a year younger. How old is she?

74

It's a fact! The number of people who live in a place is called its population. The population of the entire world is almost seven billion (7,000,000,000)!

Picture Clue
Quiz 43
Question 1

6 What is the missing number:
8 + 12 = ?

20

7 What shapes would you get if you cut a circle in half?

Two semi-circles

8 One thousand people live in Puddletown, and 200 live in Fernville. Which place has more people?

Puddletown

9 What is 10 more than 74?

84

10 Ava measured her finger. It was seven units. What units was Ava using – centimetres or metres?

Centimetres

Quiz 45 · Number Crunchers

1 How much does an egg weigh – 100 grams or 100 kilograms?

100 grams

2 What is the missing number: 20 – 10 = ?

10

3 What would you use to find out how heavy you are – a measuring jug or weighing scales?

Weighing scales

4 A frog leaps 10 centimetres at a time. How far has it travelled after five leaps?

50 centimetres

5 What is 3 more than 20?

23

It's a fact! The fastest animal in the world is the peregrine falcon. It can dive and swoop at around 200 kilometres an hour!

Picture Clue
Quiz 46
Question 5

6 Which shape has 6 sides – a pentagon or a hexagon?

A hexagon

7 Max has four 50 pence coins, and his sister Molly has five 20 pence coins. Who has most money?

Max, he has £2. Molly only has £1

8 What is the next number in this sequence: 3, 6, 9 ...?

12

9 A postman delivers 3 parcels to Mr Fox, 5 parcels to Miss Fox and 2 to Mrs Fox. Who has the most?

Miss Fox

10 An eagle flies at 50 kilometres an hour, but a falcon flies at 75 kilometres an hour. Which bird flies fastest?

The falcon

Quiz 46 • Number Crunchers

QUESTIONS

ANSWERS

1. Which weighs more – one kilogram of feathers or one kilogram of pebbles?

They weigh the same, one kilogram

2. What is 10 more than 90?

100

3. Which shape beginning with D has 4 sides, 2 lines of symmetry but no right angles?

A diamond

4. What is the next even number in this sequence: 8, 6, 4 ...?

2

5. Henry's birthday is in May. Gemma's birthday is 2 months later. What month is Gemma's birthday?

July

It's a fact! The Romans named some of their months after gods and goddesses. January is named after the god Janus, and June is named after the goddess Juno. July was named after Julius Caesar.

Picture Clue
Quiz 45 Question 3

6. What is 10 less than 31?

21

7. School finished at 3 o'clock but Mum was an hour late to collect Adam. What time did she arrive?

4 o'clock

8. Halve 12 and add one. What is the answer?

7

9. Pete flies to Paris on Monday and comes home five days later. What day does he come back?

Saturday

10. A gorilla finds 8 bananas and shares them equally with 4 friends. How many bananas do they get each?

2

QUESTIONS

ANSWERS

1 What is the next number in this sequence: 10, 20, 30, 40 …?

50

2 What is the missing number: 13 + ? = 20

7

3 Double 50 and add one. What do you get?

101

4 Ben knows 9 songs, and Chloe has learnt 3 of them. How many more does Chloe need to learn?

6

5 There were 12 chocolates in the box, before Uncle Bob ate 3 of them. How many are left?

9

It's a fact! The people of India invented modern numbers. They even invented zero so we would have a way to show when there were no units, or tens, in a number.

Picture Clue
Quiz 48
Question 8

6 You need 200 grams of flour to make a cake and half as much butter. How much butter is needed?

100 grams

7 How many right angles are there in a square?

4

8 What is 1 less than 11?

10

9 Which of these numbers is odd: 12, 6, 7, 24 or 10?

7

10 Anesu had 8 tennis balls, but he lost 6 of them. How many does he have left?

2

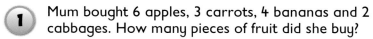

Quiz 48 • Number Crunchers

1 Mum bought 6 apples, 3 carrots, 4 bananas and 2 cabbages. How many pieces of fruit did she buy?

> 10 – only apples and bananas are fruits

2 What is the missing number: ? + 15 = 20

> 5

3 Put these units in order of size, from smallest to largest: kilometre, millimetre, centimetre.

> Millimetre, centimetre, kilometre

4 Morning play lasts for 20 minutes and it begins at 11 o'clock. What time will play finish?

> Twenty past eleven, or 11.20

5 What is 10 more than 45?

> 55

It's a fact! The ancient Egyptians were good at telling the time by using the Sun, stars and Moon. It is thanks to the Egyptians that we divide our days into 24 hours.

Picture Clue
Quiz 47
Question 5

6 Paul had 20 teeth, but two of them fell out. How many did he have left?

> 18

7 Halve 8, add 6 and double the answer. What do you get?

> 20

8 A tandem is a bicycle for 2 people. How many tandems do you need for 6 people?

> 3

9 Milly and Jack have made 6 flapjacks. Both eat half – how many do they get each?

> 3

10 How many minutes are there in one hour?

> 60

Quiz 49 • Number Crunchers

High Five!

Here are ten sums, all containing the number 5.

Are the answers correct or wrong?

1 $5 + 5 = 10$

2 $3 \times 5 = 20$

3 $10 - 5 = 5$

4 $20 \div 5 = 5$

5 $25 - 5 = 20$

6 $5 \times 5 = 25$

7 $20 \times 5 = 125$

8 $10 \times 5 = 55$

9 $15 \div 5 = 3$

10 $5 + 75 = 80$

Quiz 50 • Number Crunchers

What Shape am I?

Can you name the shapes?

The first five are 3D shapes and the second five are 2D shapes.

1

2

3

4

5

6

7

8

9

10

Quiz 51 • Our World

QUESTIONS

ANSWERS

1 Is the United Kingdom in America or Europe?

Europe

2 What word beginning with Z is a stripy animal you might find in Africa?

Zebra

3 Which of these is not a planet: Mars, Hera, Jupiter or Venus?

Hera

4 Is the Sun made of burning gases or boiling liquids?

Burning gases

5 What word beginning with O is the gas in our atmosphere that we breathe?

Oxygen

It's a fact! Mars is a cold, rocky planet covered in red sand and frozen ice caps. It is home to Olympus Mons, the largest volcano in the Solar System.

Picture Clue
Quiz 52
Question 5

6 Is lightning caused by electricity or rainbows?

Electricity

7 What do you take if you break up from school, or go on a trip away?

A holiday

8 Is a canal a waterway or a type of train track?

A waterway

9 What name is given to the low land between mountains – a tunnel or a valley?

A valley

10 What name is given to the largest, or most important, city in a country?

Capital

Quiz 52 • Our World

QUESTIONS

ANSWERS

1 What word beginning with A is a book you would use to look at maps of different countries?

Atlas

2 How would you say 'hello' to a French person?

Bonjour

3 What season follows autumn?

Winter

4 If you had a job as a choreographer would you work with builders or dancers?

Dancers

5 What word beginning with R means to use things again, or change them to make new things?

Recycle

It's a fact! Volcanoes are openings in the Earth's surface. Hot rock, called lava, can flow out through these openings. Volcanoes are often cone-shaped, and they are found under the sea as well as on land.

Picture Clue
Quiz 51
Question 2

6 What black-and-white bear might you find in China?

Giant panda

7 Where is the Arctic – the North Pole or the South Pole?

The North Pole

8 What word beginning with L is the hot, liquid rock that flows out of volcanoes?

Lava

9 Are the Alps lakes or mountains?

Mountains

10 Is a swamp a wet place or a dry place?

A wet place

Quiz 53 • Our World

1 What is the capital city of Northern Ireland?

Belfast

2 What word beginning with R is flowing water where people can travel on boats or go fishing?

River

3 How many colours are in a rainbow?

Seven

4 What word beginning with D is a hot, dry place with lots of sand?

Desert

5 Is Africa a country or a continent?

A continent

It's a fact! Rainbows are caused by sunlight and rain. When light passes through raindrops it is split into seven colours – violet, indigo, blue, green, yellow, orange and red, which we see as a rainbow.

Picture Clue
Quiz 54
Question 4

6 What would you look at to choose a holiday – a dictionary or a brochure?

A brochure

7 What word beginning with T would you use to look at the stars?

Telescope

8 Is the Sun a star or a planet?

A star

9 Does chocolate come from cocoa beans or coconut trees?

Cocoa beans

10 What word beginning with S is a big shop that not only sells food, but lots of other things too?

Supermarket

Quiz 54 • Our World

1 What word beginning with U is the name for world, the planets and everything in space?

Universe

2 Where is the Amazon River – South America or Africa?

South America

3 What word beginning with B is a type of house that has no upper floor?

Bungalow

4 You are in the city of Rome. Which country are you in?

Italy

5 Is India in Europe or Asia?

Asia

It's a fact! The biggest river in the world is the Amazon in South America. It carries more water than any other river, but the River Nile in Africa is longer.

Picture Clue
Quiz 53
Question 7

6 Which country is closer to the North Pole – the UK or Greece?

The UK

7 What word beginning with G is the type of warming that is making the world hotter?

Global

8 How many people live in the city of New York – eight thousand or eight million?

Eight million

9 What word beginning with F is a piece of farmland where farmers grow their crops?

Field

10 Where would you see the Eiffel Tower – New York or Paris?

Paris

Quiz 55 • Our World

1 What is the capital of Spain – Madrid or Rome?

Madrid

2 What do people usually travel in to reach an island – a boat or a train?

A boat

3 What word beginning with M is a big road where traffic travels at high speed?

Motorway

4 Is the Nile a volcano or a river?

A river

5 Which is bigger – a city or a town?

A city

It's a fact! The Pacific Ocean is one of the five oceans in the world. The others are the Atlantic, Indian, Southern and Arctic oceans. All oceans have salty water and they are home to billions of living things.

Picture Clue
Quiz 56
Question 9

6 What word beginning with W is a place where a river falls over high rocks?

Waterfall

7 Where do people go if they are unwell or have been hurt in an accident?

Hospital

8 What is the largest ocean – the Pacific or the Indian?

The Pacific

9 Where would you see a tropical rainforest – Brazil or Poland?

Brazil

10 What is the capital city of Scotland?

Edinburgh

Quiz 56 • Our World

1 What do we call houses that are attached to other houses on both sides – joined or terraced?

Terraced

2 What word beginning with H is a place people stay in when they are on holiday?

Hotel

3 In the UK, which day has the most hours of sunshine – 21st June or 21st December?

21st June

4 Can car tyres be recycled?

Yes

5 What is the capital city of Wales?

Cardiff

It's a fact! The country of Japan is made up of more than 6000 islands. Many of the islands have mountains and volcanoes, and Japan sometimes has earthquakes.

Picture Clue
Quiz 55
Question 6

6 What name is given to the fluffy-looking white shapes in the sky?

Clouds

7 Is the country of Japan in Asia or Europe?

Asia

8 Is the United States governed by a king or a president?

A president

9 What name is given to land that is surrounded by water on all sides – a cliff or an island?

An island

10 When there is a heatwave is the weather very hot or very cold?

Very hot

Quiz 57 • Our World

1 What does a greengrocer sell?

Fruit and vegetables

2 What is the capital city of England?

London

3 What is the world's largest country – India or Russia?

Russia

4 What type of habitat is the Sahara – a desert or a sea?

A desert

5 What name is given to the pieces of frozen water that sometimes fall from the sky?

Hail

It's a fact! People use vehicles such as cars, trains and motorbikes to get from one place to another. The first vehicles were probably boats, and carts that were pulled by horses or people.

Picture Clue
Quiz 58
Question 4

6 Where do Brazil nuts come from – Africa or South America?

South America

7 How would you say 'hello' in Spanish?

Hola

8 Which of these vehicles is not a type of aircraft: helicopter, plane, hovercraft, hot air balloon?

Hovercraft

9 Where might you see the Mekong River – Chile or China?

China

10 Is Ben Nevis a city or a mountain?

A mountain

Quiz 58 • Our World

1 What is the capital of France – Paris or Madrid?

Paris

2 What place do you go to when you are about to take a plane journey?

Airport

3 Do rivers flow away from the sea or towards the sea?

Towards the sea

4 Which of these animals does not live in grasslands: rhino, penguin, lion, deer?

Penguin

5 Which country would you be in if you went to Disney World, Florida?

The United States

It's a fact! Mount Snowdon in Wales is Britain's second tallest mountain. The tallest mountain is called Ben Nevis and it is in Scotland. England's tallest mountain is called Scafell Pike.

Picture Clue
Quiz 57
Question 8

6 What word beginning with T is a temporary home for campers?

Tent

7 Where might you eat fish and chips, buy some rock, paddle in the water and play in the sand?

At the seaside

8 Where is Mount Snowdon – Wales or Scotland?

Wales

9 What is the name of the rocky ball that travels around the Earth?

The Moon

10 Which country is famous for its pasta dishes – Germany or Italy?

Italy

Quiz 59 • Our World

What's the Weather?

Can you match the different weather conditions with the pictures below?

Clouds, hurricane, ice, lightning, mist, rain, rainbow, snow, sunshine, tornado.

Quiz 60 • Our World

Get Mapping!

This map of the British Isles has ten numbers on it. Look at the list of place names and see if you can match them to the numbers.

England

Scotland

Wales

Northern Ireland

London

Edinburgh

Cardiff

Belfast

English Channel

North Sea

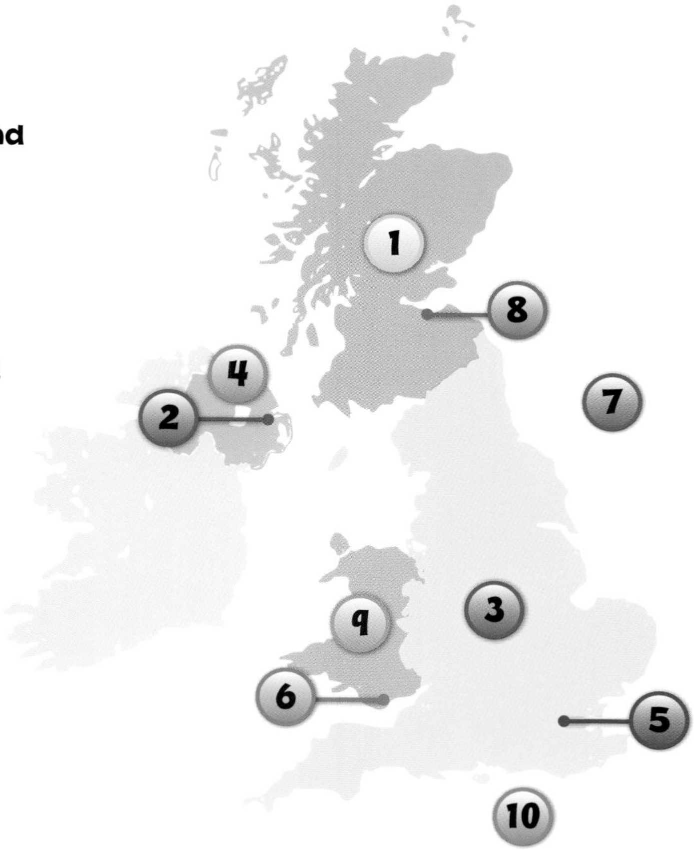

1

8

4

2

7

9

3

6

5

10

Quiz 61 • Past Times

1 What word beginning with M is a building where you can go to learn about the past?

Museum

2 What was the biggest city on Earth 2000 years ago – Rome or London?

Rome

3 What word beginning with C means 100 years – cemetery or century?

Century

4 According to legend, which King of England pulled a sword from a stone – Arthur or James?

Arthur

5 What was the name of the famous nurse who helped soldiers in the Crimean War?

Florence Nightingale

It's a fact! The Egyptians wrote on papyrus, a type of paper made from reeds. Strips of papyrus were laid in rows on a frame in layers, pressed, dried and finally smoothed.

Picture Clue
Quiz 62
Question 8

6 Which ancient people used papyrus to make paper?

The ancient Egyptians

7 When did the First World War begin – 1814 or 1914?

1914

8 How many wives did Henry the Eighth have?

Six

9 Which British queen ruled for more than 60 years – Victoria or Anne?

Victoria

10 Which year came first – 1895 or 1985?

1895

Quiz 62 • Past Times

1 Who lived first – the Tudors or the Victorians?

The Tudors

2 What country did the Romans come from – Italy or France?

Italy

3 Did the Vikings sail in longships or canoes?

Longships

4 Florence Nightingale was born in 1820 and she died 90 years later. What year did she die in?

1910

5 Did the Second World War take place in Roman times, or modern times?

Modern times

It's a fact! Vikings attacked England around 1300 years ago. They travelled from northern Europe in boats called longships.

Picture Clue
Quiz 61
Question 4

6 What name was given to the blue denim trousers that were invented for cowboys and gold miners?

Jeans

7 What title is given to the daughter of a king or queen?

Princess

8 Who was kept in prison for 27 years and became South Africa's first black president?

Nelson Mandela

9 Was the Spitfire a plane or a tank that was used in the Second World War?

A plane

10 What name is given to a picture taken with a camera that can tell us about the past?

A photograph

Quiz 63 • Past Times

1 Was Isaac Newton a great scientist or a great artist?

A great scientist

2 Was Queen Cleopatra queen of England or queen of Egypt?

Queen of Egypt

3 Did the Anglo-Saxons have electricity?

No, they didn't, it hadn't been invented

4 What was invented first – the bicycle or the television?

The bicycle

5 Do people write or paint in a diary?

Write

It's a fact! The first bicycles didn't have pedals or rubber wheels, so they were uncomfortable to ride. Bicycles with big front wheels were called penny farthings.

Picture Clue
Quiz 64
Question 2

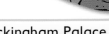

6 Where does Queen Elizabeth the Second live – Cardiff Castle or Buckingham Palace?

Buckingham Palace

7 What name was given to a Roman leader – emperor or prime minister?

Emperor

8 Who defeated King Harold at the Battle of Hastings in 1066?

William the Conqueror

9 What did Stone Age people use to make their tools – stones or metal?

Stones

10 Which country did Bonnie Prince Charlie fight for – Scotland or Wales?

Scotland

Quiz 64 · Past Times

QUESTIONS

ANSWERS

1. In which country did the Olympic Games begin – Greece or Italy?

Greece

2. What word beginning with P were giant tombs built by the ancient Egyptians?

Pyramids

3. When did the Second World War begin – 1939 or 1979?

1939

4. What were the traditional homes of North American Indians called – pootoos or teepees?

Teepees

5. When were cars invented – around 100 years ago or 30 years ago?

100 years ago

It's a fact! The Olympic Games take place every two years and there are both summer and winter games. Thousands of athletes from around the world take part to try and win bronze, silver or gold medals.

Picture Clue
Quiz 63
Question 6

6. An old longship was buried at Sutton Hoo. Who buried it there – Vikings or Romans?

Vikings

7. Were children who were moved to safety in the Second World War called nominees or evacuees?

Evacuees

8. What name is given to a military man who wore armour, rode a horse and took part in jousts?

Knight

9. Which English city burned down in the Great Fire of 1666?

London

10. Where were steam trains invented – Britain or Russia?

Britain

Quiz 65 • Past Times

QUESTIONS

1 Which city was attacked by warriors who hid inside a giant wooden horse – Paris or Troy?

2 Who was the Roman god of war – Mars or Neptune?

3 Which doctor helped poor Victorian children – Dr Barnardo or Dr Jessop?

4 What item of clothing did ancient Romans wear – a toga or a yoga?

5 In which city would you find the Colosseum – Paris or Rome?

It's a fact! We can learn about the past by looking at objects from long ago. Archaeologists (say: ark-ee-olo-jists) search for clues, such as coins and jewellery, from the past.

6 Was Mozart good at writing music or writing books?

7 Was Boudicca a Celtic queen or a Roman queen?

8 Which country did King Tutankhamun rule?

9 What word beginning with S were used by soldiers in battle to protect themselves?

10 Which tool would be more useful to an archaeologist – a spade or a screwdriver?

ANSWERS

Troy

Mars

Dr Barnardo

A toga

Rome

Picture Clue
Quiz 66
Question 1

Writing music

A Celtic queen

Egypt

Shields

A spade

Quiz 66 • Past Times

QUESTIONS

ANSWERS

1 Who was the first man to step foot on the Moon – Neil Armstrong or Buzz Aldrin?

Neil Armstrong

2 Which name beginning with Z was the ancient Greeks' king of the gods?

Zeus

3 Where would you see a stone circle called Stonehenge – in England or Wales?

England

4 Which ocean did European explorers have to cross to reach America?

The Atlantic Ocean

5 Who was Christopher Columbus?

He was a great explorer

It's a fact! The first men to visit the Moon started their journey in a giant rocket called Saturn V (5). The rocket was seven times heavier than than a fully-loaded jumbo jet!

Picture Clue
Quiz 65
Question 9

6 When is American Independence Day – July the 4th or January the 1st?

July the 4th

7 Was Julius Caesar a Roman or a Victorian?

A Roman

8 What name is given to the special chair on which kings and queens sit?

Throne

9 What century are we living in now – the 20th century or the 21st century?

The 21st century

10 What is the name for a toy bear that became popular about 100 years ago?

Teddy

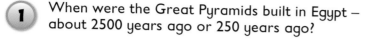

Quiz 67 • Past Times

1 When were the Great Pyramids built in Egypt – about 2500 years ago or 250 years ago?

About 2500 years ago

2 Was Leonardo da Vinci a great artist and scientist, or a singer and dancer?

A great artist and scientist

3 In what year did people first walk on the Moon – 1969 or 2009?

1969

4 Where did the Great Fire of London start – in Pudding Lane or Ice Cream Lane?

Pudding Lane

5 Which ancient people were famous for making mummies?

The Egyptians

It's a fact! Mummies are dead bodies that have not rotted away. The best known artificial mummies were made in ancient Egypt. The Egyptians even mummified animals such as cats, dogs, monkeys and crocodiles.

Picture Clue
Quiz 68
Question 7

6 Where did the Aztecs live – America or Australia?

America

7 William the Conqueror invaded England in 1066. What country was he from – France or Japan?

France

8 Who wrote the play *Romeo and Juliet* – William Shakespeare or Andrew Lloyd Webber?

William Shakespeare

9 Which ancient people invented the theatre – the Greeks or the Vikings?

The Greeks

10 Did children play computer games 50 years ago?

No, they hadn't been invented

Quiz 68 • Past Times

1 What was Enid Blyton famous for – writing children's books or making children's clothes?

Writing children's books

2 What word beginning with V is the name given to a Roman home?

Villa

3 Whose army used elephants to cross the Alps – Henry the Eighth's or Hannibal's?

Hannibal's

4 Who tried to blow up the Houses of Parliament – Guy Fawkes or William Turner?

Guy Fawkes

5 What was the strongest part of a castle – the keep or the safe?

The keep

It's a fact! The Great Fire of London lasted for four days and four nights. The fire destroyed about 13,000 houses and 87 churches. Amazingly, only six people died in the fire.

Picture Clue
QUIZ 67
Question 5

6 Was Pocahontas a Native American princess or an Egyptian servant girl?

A Native American princess

7 Would Victorian children watch Punch and Judy shows at the seaside or at school?

At the seaside

8 Which birds died out soon after explorers came to their island home – chiffchaffs or dodos?

Dodos

9 What was Christopher Columbus famous for – exploring or farming?

Exploring

10 George Stephenson built one of the first trains. Was it called *Rocket* or *Racket*?

Rocket

Quiz 69 • Past Times

Step Back in Time

All of these pictures come from different time periods.

Can you say if they are from Greek, Roman, Celtic, Viking or Victorian times?

1

2

3

4

5

6

7

8

9

10

A Viking Longhouse

More than 1000 years ago, Vikings lived in Britain
in longhouses. Look at the ten labels below.

Can you match each label to the numbers on the house?

Turf (earth with growing grass) roof

Outside toilet

Meat was smoked to preserve it

Loom for weaving cloth

Stable

Walls were made of logs

Wooden rafters

Hearth (fireplace)

Weapons on walls

Hole for smoke to escape

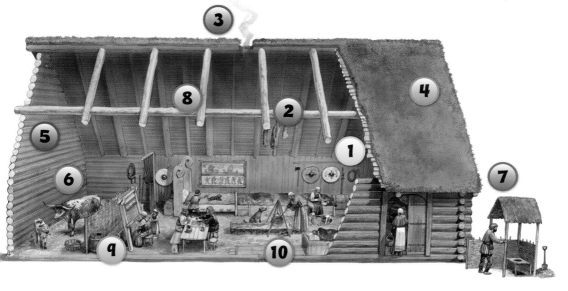

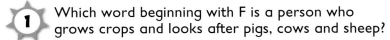

Quiz 71 • How We Live

1 Which word beginning with F is a person who grows crops and looks after pigs, cows and sheep?

Farmer

2 If a person comes from Spain are they Scottish or Spanish?

Spanish

3 What is an important symbol for Christians — a cross or a circle?

A cross

4 On the radio, what name is given to the person who plays the music?

Disc jockey, or DJ

5 Is Beyoncé best known as a singer or fashion designer?

A singer

It's a fact! Skyscrapers are the tallest buildings. The first one was built in the United States in the 1880s. It had ten storeys, or floors. Today they can be 500 metres tall and have more than 100 storeys.

Picture Clue
Quiz 72
Question 1

6 Is a skyscraper a tall building or a type of plane?

A tall building

7 If Tony's son has a daughter, is she Tony's granddaughter or step-daughter?

His granddaughter

8 What word beginning with W is the money someone gets paid for doing a job?

Wage

9 If you paint a picture of yourself, what type of portrait is it?

A self portrait

10 Where are cars made — in galleries or factories?

Factories

Quiz 72 • How We Live

QUESTIONS

ANSWERS

1 Which people live near the North Pole – Indians or the Inuit?

The Inuit

2 What word beginning with N is a person who helps doctors look after the sick?

Nurse

3 Which sport is most popular in China – table tennis or snooker?

Table tennis

4 Complete the name of Miley Cyrus's famous character: Hannah...

Montana

5 Is New Year's Day a Bank Holiday in the UK?

Yes

It's a fact! Miley Cyrus is an actress and singer born in the United States in 1992. She began performing when she very young and first appeared on TV with her father, who is also a singer.

Picture Clue
Quiz 71
Question 1

6 Would you walk or sail on a canal?

Sail, it's a man-made waterway

7 What word beginning with A tells people where you live?

Address

8 What is the most important book in the Christian faith – the Bible or the Qur'an?

The Bible

9 When do you need a passport – when you go abroad or when you visit the doctor?

When you go abroad

10 Is a hammock used for cooking or sleeping?

Sleeping

Quiz 73 · How We Live

1 What word beginning with T is a person who helps others, especially children, to learn?

Teacher

2 What do you call someone who learns about how the world works – a celebrity or a scientist?

A scientist

3 When do Australians take their summer holidays – in December or July?

December

4 What word beginning with P is a beautiful building that kings and queens live in?

Palace

5 Where does the footballer Ryan Giggs come from – France or Wales?

Wales

It's a fact! The first ambulances were horse-drawn wagons. The first motorized ambulance was used in 1899. Today, ambulances are speedy vehicles that are fitted with the latest medical equipment.

Picture Clue
Quiz 74
Question 1

6 What word beginning with P is a place people visit to walk their dogs, play sport or relax?

Park

7 Is your mother's mother your grandmother or your great-aunt?

Grandmother

8 What is the name of the vehicle that picks up sick or injured people and takes them to hospital?

Ambulance

9 Are sledges used to travel over ice and snow or cut down trees?

To travel over ice and snow

10 Which people worship the god Krishna – Hindus or Jews?

Hindus

Quiz 74 • How We Live

1 What word beginning with F is a person who puts out fires and teaches people about fire safety?

Firefighter

2 What word beginning with D is a musical instrument that you hit with sticks?

Drum

3 Which autumn festival celebrates farmers and the food they grow?

Harvest festival

4 On what date is Christmas Day celebrated?

25th December

5 What word beginning with M is a building that Muslims go to celebrate the end of Ramadan?

Mosque

It's a fact! Sometimes fires start in forests or woodlands. These fires can spread so quickly that special planes are used to dump water on them from overhead.

Picture Clue
Quiz 73
Question 4

6 Is Harry Potter a real person, or a character in a book?

A character in a book

7 How many people live in Japan's largest city, Tokyo – 34 million or 14 million?

34 million

8 What word beginning with W is a ceremony that takes place when two people get married?

Wedding

9 What is the greatest age that any person has lived to – 122 years or 112 years?

122 years

10 What is the special meal that Jews eat to celebrate Passover – Thanksgiving or Seder?

Seder

Quiz 75 • How We Live

1 If someone cuts people's hair for a living, what is their job title?

Hairdresser or barber

2 What musical instrument beginning with P has keys that are pressed to make sound?

Piano

3 What is an important symbol for Jewish people – a cross or a Star of David?

A Star of David

4 When might people decorate their homes with pumpkins?

At Halloween

5 What place would you go to enjoy plays and concerts?

Theatre

It's a fact! The Internet allows computers all over the world to connect to each other. We use the Internet to see web pages, use email, play games and download music.

Picture Clue
Quiz 76 Question 3

6 What is a souvenir – a keepsake or a type of seashell?

A keepsake

7 What is the UK's biggest city?

London

8 To play a game on the Internet do you have to be online or underline?

Online

9 What would you use to listen to music – an MP3 player or a BC5 player?

MP3 player

10 What would you call your father's brother – aunt or uncle?

Uncle

Quiz 76 • How We Live

1 Which of these foods is a vegetable: courgette, lemon, banana?

Courgette

2 What is the name of the Hindu elephant god — Krishna or Ganesh?

Ganesh

3 Would you use the London Underground to travel by train or by bus?

To travel by train

4 Is a hobby something people do for pleasure or as a household chore?

Something people do for pleasure

5 What piece of jewellery do people give each other when they get married?

A ring

It's a fact! Ice cream is the most popular frozen dessert in the world. Vanilla, is the most popular flavour, with chocolate coming a close second!

Picture Clue
Quiz 75
Question 3

6 How many people are in the pop group, McFly?

Four

7 Where would go to catch a train?

A train station

8 Who eats the most ice cream — Australians or Americans?

Australians

9 What is a theme park — a place with rides and games or a music centre?

A place with rides and games

10 What word beginning with D is the Hindu festival that is also known as the Festival of Lights?

Diwali

Quiz 77 • How We Live

1 At what time of year do people eat chocolate eggs?

Easter

2 What word beginning with C is worn on the heads of royalty, especially kings and queens?

Crown

3 If you are flying a plane, what job title do you have?

Pilot

4 When people get older they give up work. Are they returfed or retired?

Retired

5 What do people read to find out what has been happening around the world?

A newspaper

It's a fact! In Britain, and some other countries, 26th December is called Boxing Day. It was once tradition that servants and the poor were given the day off work, and a gift, in a box, or some money.

Picture Clue
Quiz 78
Question 3

6 What is the most important book in the Jewish faith – the Torah or the Bible?

The Torah

7 What word beginning with A is a person who performs in plays, films or television programmes?

Actor or actress

8 What is the name of the day after Christmas Day?

Boxing Day

9 In France, what does 'bonjour' mean?

Hello

10 What type of pet is also known as 'man's best friend' – dog or cat?

Dog

Quiz 78 • How We Live

QUESTIONS

1. Where might you find a lifeguard?
2. Where do Christians pray – in churches or in temples?
3. Are people who travel to other places on holiday called florists or tourists?
4. Where would you go to watch a new film?
5. What is the most important book in the Islamic faith – the Bible or the Qur'an?

It's a fact! In 1989, cartoonist Matt Groening created The Simpsons, which is America's longest running cartoon show. Children and adults enjoy watching the Simpsons' adventures.

6. What language did the ancient Romans use – Latin or Bengali?
7. Are the Pussycat Dolls a pop group or girls' toys?
8. Which yellow family appears in a famous American cartoon show?
9. A sari is a dress traditionally worn by women from which country – Norway or India?
10. What would you do in a restaurant – eat a meal or buy groceries?

ANSWERS

1. By a swimming pool or at the beach
2. Churches
3. Tourists
4. The cinema
5. The Qur'an

Picture Clue
Quiz 77
Question 2

6. Latin
7. A pop group
8. The Simpsons
9. India
10. Eat a meal

Musical Match-up

These musical instruments fall into four groups:
percussion, wind, keyboard or string.

Can you tell which instrument belongs to which group?

1 Castanets

2 Xylophone

3 Flute

4 Piano

5 Double bass

6 Trumpet

7 Triangle

8 Violin

9 Drums

10 Guitar

ANSWERS 1. Percussion 2. Percussion 3. Wind 4. Keyboard 5. String 6. Wind 7. Wind 8. String 9. Percussion 10. String

Sweet or Savoury?

Look at these foods.

Can you tell which ones are sweet
and which ones are savoury?

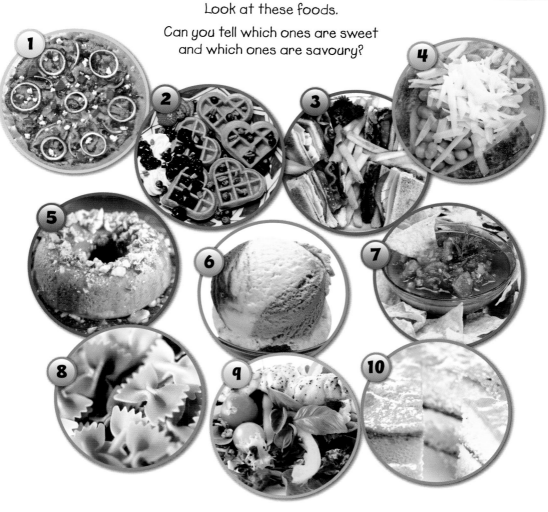

Quiz 81 • True or False

1 There are 30 seconds in half of a minute. — True

2 Plants grow from seeds. — True

3 The native people of Australia are called Aborigines. — True

4 Eating too much fat is bad for you. — True

5 'Beautiful' is a describing word. — True

It's a fact! The Black Death was a type of disease called the plague. It was carried by fleas that lived on rats. People who caught the plague usually died.

Picture Clue
Quiz 82
Question 4

6 St Andrew is the Patron Saint of Scotland. — True

7 Most of Australia is desert. — True

8 The Black Death killed 25 million people nearly 700 years ago. — True

9 A group of sheep is called a fluke. — False – it is called a flock

10 People used to believe that the Sun moved around the Earth. — True

Quiz 82 • True or False

QUESTIONS

ANSWERS

1. Snakes are a type of reptile.

   True

2. The ancient Romans wore long tunics called togas.

   True

3. Sausages, bacon and egg make a well-balanced meal.

   False – there are no fruit or vegetables

4. Butterflies have six legs, so they are insects.

   True

5. The world's first aeroplane was built by the Wright Brothers.

   True

It's a fact! Vincent van Gogh was a Dutch artist who was born in 1853. His paintings were not very popular during his life. Today, Van Gogh's colourful pictures sell for millions of pounds.

Picture Clue
Quiz 81
Question 9

6. Some bluebells are pink.

   True

7. Hail is a type of frozen rain.

   True

8. Plants get all their food from the soil.

   False – plants make their own food

9. Vincent van Gogh was an artist who created a painting called *The Sunflowers*.

   True

10. A plant's stem carries water to the flowers and leaves.

    True

Quiz 83 • True or False

1 In 1647, an English leader called Oliver Cromwell banned Christmas Day.

True

2 All poems have to rhyme.

False – lots of poems don't rhyme at all

3 When Lucy is dragging her toy pram behind her, she's using a pulling force.

True

4 School starts at 8.25 a.m. but Jack is five minutes late when he arrives at 9.00 a.m.

False – he is 35 minutes late

5 It takes about 11 muscles in your face to make a smile.

True

It's a fact! Christians celebrate Christmas on 25th December every year. It is a time when people remember the birth of Jesus Christ. People share meals, decorate trees and give presents.

Picture Clue
Quiz 84
Question 4

6 Europe is bigger than Asia.

False – Asia is much bigger

7 Long ago, children had to climb up chimneys to sweep them clean.

True

8 Grown-ups need more sleep than children.

False

9 Mary Queen of Scots lived in Tudor times.

True

10 The First World War started in 1984.

False – it started in 1914

Quiz 84 • True or False

1 Blackfoot, Cree and Cheyenne are tribes of Native Americans.

True

2 Portugal is a country in Europe.

True

3 Adolf Hitler was the leader of Germany during the Second World War.

True

4 Snakes are slimy and wet.

False – they are smooth and dry

5 Chess is a game that uses playing cards.

False – it is played on a board with pieces

It's a fact! The Earth has been through cold periods called ice ages. The last one was about 10,000 years ago. Animals, such as mammoths, had thick fur to keep warm.

Picture Clue
Quiz 83
Question 1

6 Drinking fizzy drinks can make you burp.

True

7 During the ice age Britain was covered in snow and ice.

True

8 Walking helps to keep you fit.

True

9 Baby cats are called catlings.

False – they are called kittens

10 Sugar gives you energy.

True

Quiz 85 · True or False

ANSWERS

1 St Liam is the Patron Saint of Ireland.

False – St Patrick is

2 Henry the Eighth had a servant whose job was to wipe his bottom.

True

3 Ice is lighter than water.

True

4 Dragonflies, pigeons, helicopters and wasps are all living things.

False – helicopters are not alive

5 Human bone is four times tougher than concrete.

True

It's a fact! Reptiles are scaly-skinned animals that lay eggs on land. Crocodiles, snakes and lizards are all types of reptile. Dinosaurs were reptiles that lived millions of years ago.

Picture Clue
Quiz 86
Question 3

6 Yasmin's mum's sister has two children. They are Yasmin's cousins.

True

7 Electric shocks can kill.

True

8 Turtles are swimming reptiles.

True

9 The French word for cheese is 'fromage'.

True

10 An iceberg is a type of lettuce.

True, but it is also a floating block of ice

Quiz 86 • True or False

QUESTIONS

ANSWERS

1 Most babies are born with no teeth.

True

2 If you double 10 and add another 10, you get 40.

False – you get 30

3 Tarantula spiders grow so big they can eat small children.

False – some can eat lizards or birds

4 Gold, silver, iron and tin are all types of metal.

True

5 Walt Disney was President of the United States of America.

False – he was a film producer

It's a fact! Antarctica is the huge, cold continent at the South Pole. Not many animals can live in Antarctica, although it is home to lots of types of penguin.

Picture Clue
Quiz 85
Question 8

6 Polar bears live in the Antarctic.

False – they live in the Arctic

7 Manchester is the capital of England.

False – London is England's capital

8 You are likely to breathe around ten million times every year.

True

9 Computers are powered by electricity.

True

10 The world's largest fish is called a tiddler.

False – a tiddler is a tiny fish

Quiz 87 • True or False

1 Vampire bats really exist.

True

2 The best place to buy meat is from a bakery.

False – you buy meat from a butchers

3 If one cup cake costs 20 pence then four cup cakes will cost 80 pence.

True

4 A parasol is a type of talking bird.

False – parasol is a type of umbrella

5 Smoking cigarettes is a great way to get healthy and strong.

False – cigarettes are bad for your health

It's a fact! Irish dancing is popular all over the world. Some dances are done with hard shoes that tap loudly as they hit the floor. Girls and boys take part in Irish dancing competitions.

Picture Clue
Quiz 88
Question 3

6 The smallest bone in your body is in your ear.

True

7 The people who live in Ireland are Irelandish.

False – they are Irish

8 If you plant a sunflower seed in spring, and give it water and light, the flower will bloom in summer.

True

9 The word 'giggling' has four letter 'g's in it.

True

10 Cuboids are 3D shapes.

True

Quiz 88 • True or False

1 Tigers mostly eat bananas and grapes.

False — they eat meat

2 Your biggest muscles are in your bottom.

True

3 The Romans built the Great Pyramids.

False — the Egyptians did

4 The Internet connects your computer with other computers.

True

5 50 is more than 45 and less than 53.

True

It's a fact! Tigers are the largest of all the big cats. They are predators, and hunt for food, such as deer. Tigers are endangered, which means there are not many left in the wild.

Picture Clue
Quiz 87
Question 4

6 A heartbeat is the sound of blood being pumped through your heart.

True

7 The head of the UK government is the Prime Emperor.

False — It is the Prime Minister

8 When people work they are paid money, which is called a salary or wage.

True

9 It is against the law to drive and talk on a mobile phone at the same time.

True

10 If an elephant flaps its wings hard enough, it can fly.

False — elephants do not have wings!

Quiz 89 • True or False

Describe the Pictures

Look at the pictures and the sentences below them.
Do the sentences describe what is happening?
Answer TRUE or FALSE.

1 This top is spinning.

2 The duckling is sinking.

3 The bee is flying.

4 The bottles are see-through.

5 The dragon has wings.

6 The time is 4.35.

7 This is a Z-ray.

8 The kitten's fur is curly.

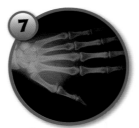

9 The tiger is striped.

10 These penguins are flying.

ANSWERS 1. True 2. False 3. True 4. True 5. True 6. False 7. False 8. False 9. True 10. False

Quiz 90 • True or False

Symmetrical or Not?

If an object is symmetrical, one half of it completely mirrors the other half. Are these objects symmetrical? Answer TRUE or FALSE.

1
2
3
4
5
6
7
8
9
10

Quiz 91 • Lucky Dip

QUESTIONS

ANSWERS

1 What colour do you get when you mix red and blue?

Purple

2 I grow very tall and I have a big yellow flower and stripy seeds. What am I?

A sunflower

3 Where do penguins live — the North Pole or the South Pole?

The South Pole

4 Double five, and add three. What answer do you get?

13

5 What date is Halloween?

31st October

It's a fact! Big Ben is the name of the bell inside the clock tower that stands next to the Houses of Parliament in London. It weighs more than 13 tonnes and is over 2 metres tall!

Picture Clue
Quiz 92
Question 2

6 What number does Thomas the Tank Engine have painted on his side?

One

7 Name the four seasons.

Spring, summer, autumn, winter

8 In P.E. Ben ran a race in 10 minutes, Joe ran it in 8 minutes and Jess ran it in 12. Who was fastest?

Joe

9 What do doctors use to see if bones are broken — Z-waves or X-rays?

X-rays

10 Where might you see Big Ben — in London or Glasgow?

London

Quiz 92 • Lucky Dip

QUESTIONS

ANSWERS

1 How many months are in one year?

12

2 I am one of your five senses and you use me to tell if something is smooth or bumpy. What am I?

Your sense of touch

3 Where will the Olympics be held in 2012?

London

4 What is the missing number: 20 − 3 = ?

17

5 Dan gets 50 pence pocket money each week. Sam gets three ten pence pieces. Who gets the most?

Dan

It's a fact! In 2008 the Summer Olympics were held in Beijing, in China. Many world records were broken. The sprinter Usain Bolt, from Jamaica, was one of the main stars.

Picture Clue
Quiz 91
Question 2

6 Who makes Wii consoles – Sony or Nintendo?

Nintendo

7 Which country was ruled by pharaohs?

Egypt

8 Which famous British sailor beat the French at the Battle of Trafalgar in 1805 – Nelson or Cook?

Nelson

9 Where would you find clubs, diamonds, hearts and spades?

On playing cards

10 Where is Norway – in Europe or Asia?

Europe

Quiz 93 • Lucky Dip

QUESTIONS

ANSWERS

1. What type of fish is Nemo?

A clownfish

2. I am put into little bags that are added to freshly boiled water to produce a hot drink. What am I?

Tea leaves

3. How many days are in a fortnight?

14

4. I was a British Queen who lived a long life and was married to Prince Albert. Who was I?

Queen Victoria

5. Which of these is not a type of dog – dalmatian, emperor, labrador or beagle?

Emperor

It's a fact! Dogs are clever animals and can be taught to understand simple commands. Dogs make good companions but they need lots of love, care and exercise.

Picture clue
Quiz 94
Question 6

6. What is the Mediterranean – a sea or a mountain?

A sea

7. What year came after 2003, and before 2005?

2004

8. What is the missing number: $16 - 8 = ?$

8

9. What word beginning with H is the study of past times and people?

History

10. I am called 'a ship of the desert' and I can go for a long time without water. What animal am I?

A camel

Quiz 94 • Lucky Dip

QUESTIONS

ANSWERS

1 What word beginning with P is liquid colour that you apply with brushes?

Paint

2 In which movie does Woody meet Buzz Lightyear?

Toy Story

3 Which cartoon builder asks 'Can we fix it?'

Bob the Builder

4 I am remembered on 5th November, when people light bonfires and fireworks. Who am I?

Guy Fawkes

5 What date is New Year's Eve?

31st December

It's a fact! Candles were invented in China about 200 BC, and the first ones were made with whale fat. Today, candles are made from paraffin, beeswax or gel. A person who makes or sells candles is called a chandler.

Picture Clue
Quiz 93
Question 10

6 In the Bible, David kills a giant with his slingshot. What was the giant's name – Gollum or Goliath?

Goliath

7 What word beginning with C has a wick, can be made of wax and provides us with light?

Candle

8 What is the fifth month of the year?

May

9 What is 5 more than 26?

31

10 What material is see-through and hard but smashes easily?

Glass

Quiz 95 • Lucky Dip

1 What is Postman Pat's black-and-white cat called?

Jess

2 I have two or three hands, a face, and I tell the time. What am I?

A clock, or a watch

3 I have one curved side, one straight side and I am a circle that has been cut in half. What am I?

A semi-circle

4 What is the name of Shaggy's pet detective?

Scooby-Doo

5 I am the country where kangaroos and koalas live. What country am I?

Australia

It's a fact! Australia is the sixth largest country in the world — about 20 million people live there. Many European families settled there long ago. Aborigines are the native people of Australia.

Picture Clue
Quiz 96
Question 4

6 I have four sides that are all the same length and four right angles. What am I?

A square

7 I am made from trees and used to make books and magazines. What am I?

Paper

8 Which season does Easter fall in — spring or autumn?

Spring

9 I am a character from a TV series. I travel through time in my TARDIS. Who am I?

Doctor Who

10 Who is the Patron Saint of Wales — St David or St Donald?

St David

Quiz 96 • Lucky Dip

QUESTIONS

1 What material is soft and warm and comes from sheep?

2 I have six legs and a stripy body. I buzz around flowers and make honey. What am I?

3 How many weeks are in one year – 100 or 52?

4 What word beginning with S is a large leather seat that riders use when sitting on a horse?

5 What equipment does Mrs Turner use to help her class bake cakes – weighing scales or a ruler?

It's a fact! Bees are insects that pollinate flowers, helping them to grow. They collect nectar from flowers and take it back to their hive to make honey, which they use to feed their young.

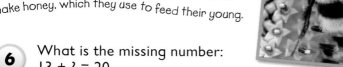

Picture Clue
Quiz 95
Question 10

6 What is the missing number:
13 + ? = 20

7 When would you watch a nativity play – at Easter or Christmas?

8 What does www stand for in an Internet address?

9 Is the Atlantic an ocean or an island?

10 What colour is SpongeBob SquarePants?

ANSWERS

Wool

A bee

52

Saddle

Weighing scales

7

Christmas

World Wide Web

An ocean

Yellow

Quiz 97 • Lucky Dip

ANSWERS

1 In the nursery rhyme, the cow jumped over the Moon, but who ran away with the spoon?

The dish

2 Is Pikachu a Power Ranger or a Pokemon?

A Pokemon

3 Was Napoleon Bonaparte a French emperor or an Italian artist?

A French emperor

4 How many days are in November – 30 or 31?

30

5 What colour do you get when you mix blue and yellow?

Green

It's a fact! Remembrance Day takes place every year on a Sunday in November. It is also known as Poppy Day. It is a time when we remember all wars, and the brave people who fought in them.

Picture Clue
Quiz 98
Question 1

6 Which pop star sang 'The Man in the Mirror', 'Thriller' and 'Billie Jean', and died in 2009?

Michael Jackson

7 What flowers do people wear on Remembrance Day?

Poppies

8 Winston was the first name of the famous British wartime leader. What was his second name?

Churchill

9 CDs are used to store information such as music or pictures, but what do the letters CD stand for?

Compact Disc

10 My father was Henry the Eighth and my mother was beheaded. I was an English queen. Who was I?

Queen Elizabeth the First

Quiz 98 • Lucky Dip

1 I am a big green ogre and my best friend is called Donkey. Who am I?

Shrek

2 What mountain beginning with E is the tallest in the world?

Mount Everest

3 Which is bigger – a gorilla or a chimpanzee?

A gorilla

4 What is the missing number: 9 + ? = 18

9

5 What would you use to play golf – a set of clubs or a pair of dice?

A set of clubs

It's a fact! Gorillas are the biggest type of ape. They look big and fierce, but are very gentle animals. Gorillas are endangered, and there are very few left living in the wild.

Picture Clue
Quiz 97
Question 1

6 What is the name of the young lion in *The Lion King*?

Simba

7 Which of these is not a place of worship – church, temple, palace or mosque?

Palace

8 Who is the Patron Saint of England – St Winston or St George?

St George

9 What would you expect to see in a gallery – plants or paintings?

Paintings

10 What word beginnng with L is a small-sized computer you can carry?

Laptop

Quiz 99 • Lucky Dip

Signs and Symbols

Can you tell what each one of these
signs and symbols means?

1

2

3

4

5

6

7

8 CANARY WHARF

9

10

Quiz 100 • Lucky Dip

Close-ups!

Look carefully at these close-up pictures. Can you guess what they are?

1

2

4

3

5

6

7

8

9

10

SCORECARDS

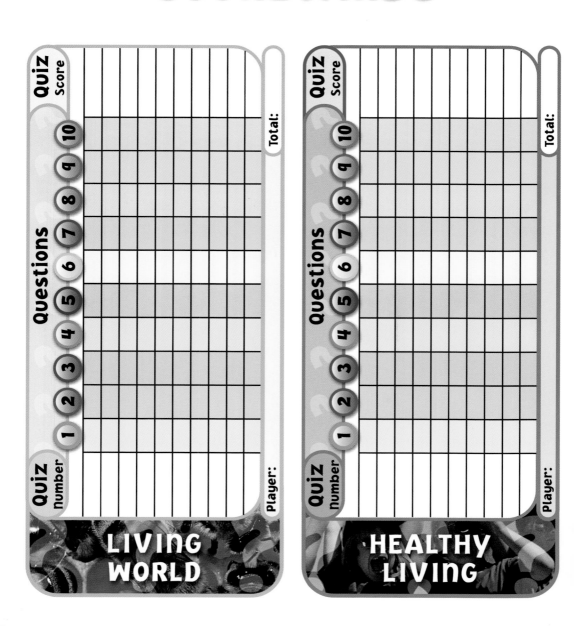

Quiz number

Questions

| 1 | 2 | 3 | 4 | 5 | 6 | 7 | 8 | 9 | 10 |

Quiz Score

Total:

Player:

LIVING WORLD

Quiz number

Questions

| 1 | 2 | 3 | 4 | 5 | 6 | 7 | 8 | 9 | 10 |

Quiz Score

Total:

Player:

HEALTHY LIVING

Photocopy the scorecards instead of writing in the book, so you can play again and again. Don't forget – for each section, you'll need one scorecard for each player. See pages 6–7 for help on how to play.

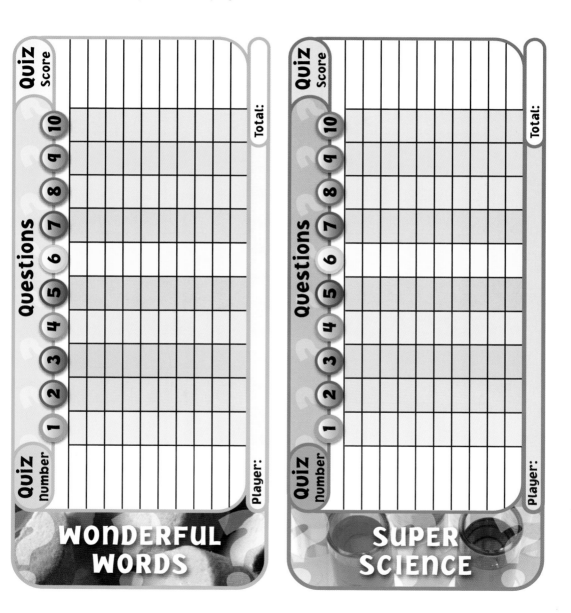

Quiz Score

Questions

Quiz number

1 2 3 4 5 6 7 8 9 10

Total:

Player:

WONDERFUL WORDS

Quiz Score

Questions

Quiz number

1 2 3 4 5 6 7 8 9 10

Total:

Player:

SUPER SCIENCE

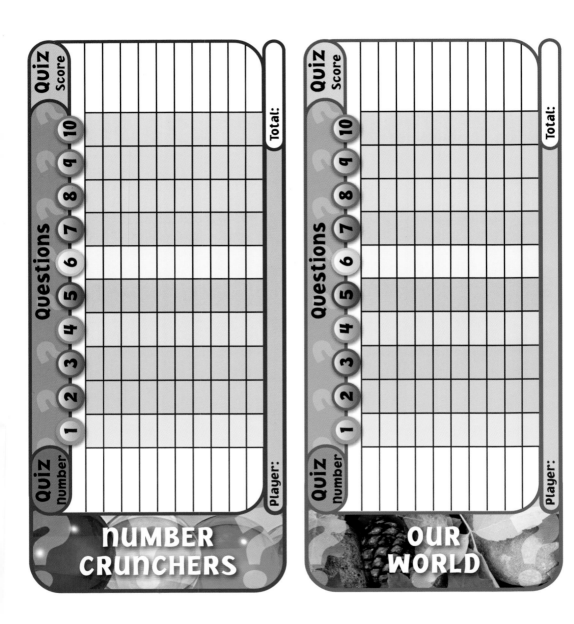

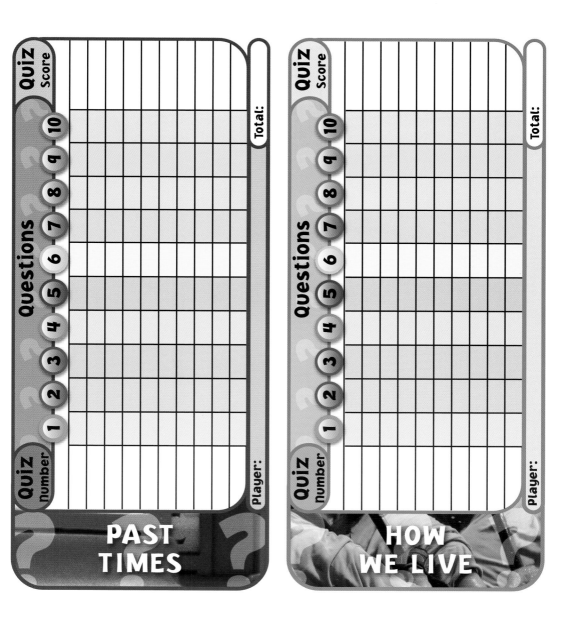

Quiz Score

Questions
1 2 3 4 5 6 7 8 9 10

Quiz number

Total:

Player:

PAST TIMES

Quiz Score

Questions
1 2 3 4 5 6 7 8 9 10

Quiz number

Total:

Player:

HOW WE LIVE

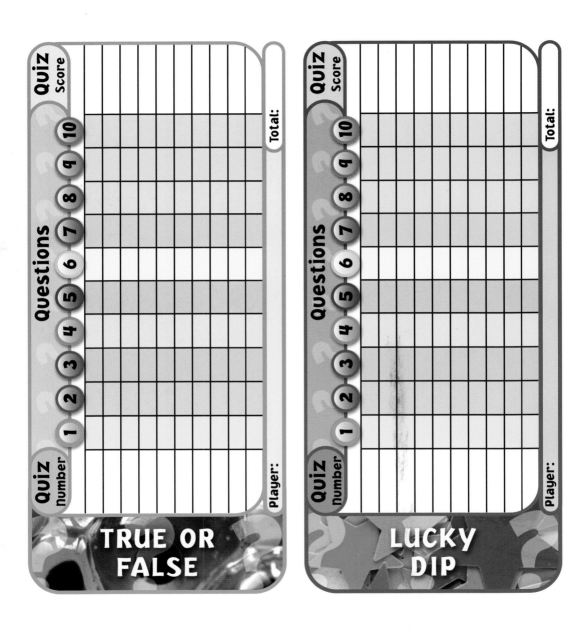

TRUE OR FALSE

Quiz number	Questions										Quiz Score
	1	2	3	4	5	6	7	8	9	10	
Player:											Total:

LUCKY DIP

Quiz number	Questions										Quiz Score
	1	2	3	4	5	6	7	8	9	10	
Player:											Total: